S0-AFN-714

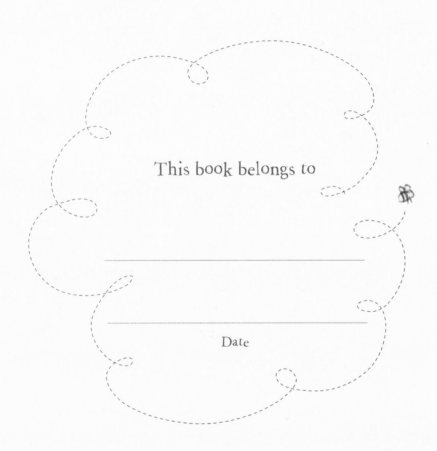

This book belongs to

_____

. . . . . . . . . . . . . . . . . . . . . . . . . . . . . . .

Date

Copyright ©Disney
Based on the "Winnie The Pooh" works by A.A. Milne and E.H. Shepard

All rights reserved.
No part of this book may be reproduced in any form or by any means, electronic or
mechanical including photocopying, recording or by any information storage and retrieval
system without the written permission of
The Walt Disney Company.
Made in China

# My Baby Book

A memory book of
the adventures and experiences
of my early years.

Sweet and new and smallish, too

Published by the C.R. Gibson Company

# "P" is for Parents . . .

Place
picture of Mommy
here

My Mommy's full name _____

_____

Birth date _____

Where she was born _____

Mommy's parents' names _____

_____

When and where they were born _____

_____

Her brothers and sisters _____

_____

Where she went to school _____

Highlights of her career _____

_____

_____

Her special talents and interests _____

_____

_____

My Daddy's full name _____

Birth date _____

Where he was born _____

Daddy's parents' names _____

_____

© Disney

# Proud as Can Be!

When and where they were born _____

_____

His brothers and sisters _____

_____

Where he went to school _____

_____

Highlights of his career _____

_____

_____

His special talents and interests _____

_____

_____

_____

_____

The story of how my Mommy and Daddy met _____

_____

_____

_____

When and where my Mommy and Daddy were married _____

_____

The honeymoon _____

_____

_____

Place
picture of Daddy
here

# A Very Grand Thing...

The day Mommy and Daddy learned the great news_____
_____
_____
_____
_____

Their reactions_____
_____
_____
_____

The first people they told_____
_____
_____
_____
_____

Their reactions_____
_____
_____
_____
_____

*Wondering is more fun with two...*

# Is About to Happen!

Due date _____

Doctor's name _____

Doctor's address _____

Cravings and aversions _____
_____

Special instructions _____
_____
_____

Prenatal test results _____
_____

Method of childbirth they chose _____
_____

Classes they attended _____
_____

Books they read _____
_____

Advice from our family and friends _____
_____
_____
_____
_____
_____
_____

© Disney

# Showers of Wishes...

Place photo here

Make a wish, little friend.

# For a Lovely Day!

Guests _____

_____

_____

_____

_____

_____

_____

_____

Gifts _____

_____

_____

_____

_____

_____

_____

_____

_____

_____

_____

_____

# Here Comes . . .

When and where labor pains began _____

_____

_____

How long labor lasted _____

Where I was born _____

People present for the delivery _____

_____

Mommy's reaction _____

_____

_____

Daddy's reaction _____

_____

_____

Memorable moments _____

_____

_____

_____

_____

_____

_____

© Disney

# A Beautiful Baby!

My Name _____

Birth date: _____    Time of birth: _____

Height: _____    Weight: _____

Color of eyes: _____    Color of hair (if any): _____

Who they thought I looked like and why _____

_____

_____

_____

Other names they considered for me _____

_____

_____

_____

How my name was chosen _____

_____

_____

_____

_____

_____

_____

_____

_____

_____

Look at you                    so small and new

# My Little Prints

Place handprints here.

Place footprints here.

My arms may be small, it's true ...

© Disney

# A Tiny Wonder

Place Birth Certificate here

Social Security Number

_____

But they're long enough                    for hugging you.

# Announcing Me

Place
birth announcement
here

_____
My birthstone

_____
My flower

Place first photos here

The wonderful things about babies is babies are wonderful things.

# The Best Baby in All the World

Place photo here

Place photo here

Who have we here? It's someone new.

# Families Are Extra Special

Place
family photo
here

© Disney

# A Family is...

"Pooh, where do babies come from?"

© Disney

# A Very Grand Thing

_____

Me

_____

Mommy

_____

Daddy

My
Brothers and
Sisters

_____

My Maternal Grandparents

_____

_____

My Paternal Grandparents

_____

My Maternal Great-Grandparents

_____

My Paternal Great-Grandparents

_____

My Maternal Great-Grandparents

_____

My Paternal Great-Grandparents

# Home Brings Happiness...

Place nursery photo here

The day I came home from the hospital _____

_____

_____

Where we lived _____

_____

My room was decorated with Baby Looney tunes. Brother helped to decorate it before I was born

© Disney

# And a Warm Feeling Inside!

Visitors _____

_____

_____

_____

_____

_____

_____

Gifts _____

_____

_____

_____

_____

_____

_____

_____

_____

_____

*Togetherness is a very grand thing.*

# Worldly Happenings...

On the day I was born...

World news and leaders _____
_____
_____
_____
_____

Local events and leaders _____
_____
_____
_____

The President _____
_____

The economy _____
_____
_____

Popular television shows _____
_____
_____

Musical groups _____
_____
_____

Popular songs _____
_____

© Disney

# When I Was Born

Famous actors and actresses _____
_____
_____
_____

Sports figures _____
_____

Fashion trends _____
_____

Popular movies _____
_____
_____

Best-sellers _____
_____
_____

The price of:

     A gallon of gas _____

     A loaf of bread _____

     A home _____

     A car _____

     A jar of honey_____

Place
postage
stamp
here

Hello there, Mr. Butterfly. How nice of you to flutter by.

# Wonder-filled Days

How I started the day _____
_____

What I ate _____
_____
_____

How often I ate throughout the day _____
_____
_____

Songs they would sing to me _____
_____
_____

Nicknames for me _____
_____
_____

I smiled when _____
_____
_____

I laughed when _____
_____
_____
_____
_____
_____

© Disney

# Sleepy Nights

How they put me to bed at night _____

_____

_____

When I couldn't sleep, they would _____

_____

When I first slept through the night _____

_____

Bedtime stories they would tell me _____

_____

Toys I would sleep with _____

_____

_____

Lullabies or music that made me fall asleep _____

_____

_____

All about my first bed _____

_____

_____

My famous excuses for getting out of bed _____

_____

_____

_____

_____

"S is for snuggling and sweeet dreams of honey"

# Visiting My Doctor

My pediatrician _____

Address _____

My first visits and reactions _____

_____

_____

_____

## Visits:

| Date | Purpose | Treatment | Notes |
|------|---------|-----------|-------|
|      |         |           |       |
|      |         |           |       |
|      |         |           |       |
|      |         |           |       |
|      |         |           |       |
|      |         |           |       |
|      |         |           |       |
|      |         |           |       |
|      |         |           |       |
|      |         |           |       |
|      |         |           |       |
|      |         |           |       |
|      |         |           |       |

# My, I've Grown!

| Date | Age | Height | % | Weight | % |
|------|-----|--------|---|--------|---|
|      |     |        |   |        |   |
|      |     |        |   |        |   |
|      |     |        |   |        |   |
|      |     |        |   |        |   |
|      |     |        |   |        |   |
|      |     |        |   |        |   |
|      |     |        |   |        |   |
|      |     |        |   |        |   |
|      |     |        |   |        |   |
|      |     |        |   |        |   |
|      |     |        |   |        |   |
|      |     |        |   |        |   |
|      |     |        |   |        |   |
|      |     |        |   |        |   |

Comments and observations _____

_____

_____

_____

_____

_____

© Disney

# Immunizations

|  |  | Date | Reaction |
|---|---|---|---|
| Diphtheria |  | | |
| Tetanus | DTP: | | |
| Pertussis |  | | |
|  |  | | |
| Polio Vaccine | OPV/IPV: | | |
|  |  | | |
| Measles |  | | |
| Mumps | MMR: | | |
| Rubella |  | | |
| Haemophilus | HIB: | | |
|  |  | | |
|  | Hepatitis B: | | |
| Pneumococcal Conjugate | PCV7: | | |
|  |  | | |
|  |  | | |
| Varicella: (Chicken pox): |  | | |
|  |  | | |
| Other: |  | | |
|  |  | | |
|  |  | | |
|  |  | | |

© Disney

# Sunshiny Smiles

Dentist's name _____

My first visit _____

My reaction _____

_____

## Dates Teeth First Appeared

| Upper | Left | Right |
|---|---|---|
| Central Incisor | _____ | _____ |
| Lateral Incisor | _____ | _____ |
| Cuspid | _____ | _____ |
| First Molar | _____ | _____ |
| Second Molar | _____ | _____ |

| Lower | Left | Right |
|---|---|---|
| Central Incisor | _____ | _____ |
| Lateral Incisor | _____ | _____ |
| Cuspid | _____ | _____ |
| First Molar | _____ | _____ |
| Second Molar | _____ | _____ |

## Dental Checkups

| Treatment: | _____ | Date: | _____ |
|---|---|---|---|
| Treatment: | _____ | Date: | _____ |
| Treatment: | _____ | Date: | _____ |
| Treatment: | _____ | Date: | _____ |

It's hard to be brave when you're very small.

# I Can Do Anything!

When I first...

Smiled _____

Slept through the night  never! _____

Held a bottle  5 days old (no kidding) _____

Rolled over _____

Crawled  2-1-06 (Wed.)     played catch 3-2-06

Sat unsupported  6 months _____

Laughed _____

Stood up  2 months / on his own for 1 min.  6months

Ate solid food  7 months - you did not want baby food. You wanted tri-tip

Waved "bye-bye" _____

Took first step with help _____     Took first step alone _____

Said "mama" _____     Said "dada" _____

Held a cup  7 months _____

Walked _____

Spoke a word _____

Bathed in tub _____

Dressed myself _____

Brushed my teeth _____

Went potty _____

Stopped wearing diapers _____

Drew a picture _____

Wrote the alphabet _____

Sang a song _____

Place
photo
here

© Disney

Made a friend _____

Took a trip _____

Wrote my name _____


My first pair of shoes _____

_____

When and where we bought them _____

_____

My first haircut _____

When and where _____

My reaction _____

## First Haircut

before

after

Place
photo
here

Place
photo
here

We'll be best friends until forever. Wait and see....

# What I Love...

My favorite...

Foods _____
_____

Toys _____

Games _____
_____

Stories _____

Lullabies _____
_____

Nursery rhymes _____
_____

Songs _____
_____

Friends _____
_____

Baby-sitters _____
_____

Relatives _____
_____
_____

Clothes _____
_____

Pets _____    Colors _____

# Honey to Hide-and-Seek

Our favorite place to walk _____

_____

_____

My favorite day trips _____

_____

_____

How I acted in the car _____

_____

_____

How I acted when we ate out _____

_____

_____

What we did on weekends _____

_____

_____

My first train or plane ride _____

_____

_____

Our first vacation together _____

_____

_____

_____

_____

© Disney

# Happy Birthday, Little Me

## It's Fun To Be 1!

How we celebrated _____

_____

My birthday outfit _____

The cake _____

My reaction _____

My gifts _____

_____

_____

Friends and family who celebrated with us _____

_____

_____

Place
first birthday
photo here

Place
first birthday
photos here

# "B" is for Birthdays . . .

## Turning 2 with Pooh!

How we celebrated my Second Birthday _____

_____

_____

_____

_____

_____

## Can It Be? I'm 3!

How we celebrated my Third Birthday _____

_____

_____

_____

_____

_____

_____

*As everyone sang "Happy Birthday"...*

*he thought his heart...*

# Bright and Sunny

## Cheers for My 4th Year!

How we celebrated my Fourth Birthday _____

_____

_____

_____

_____

_____

## It's My 5th Birthday...Hooray!

How we celebrated my Fifth Birthday _____

_____

_____

_____

_____

_____

_____

would burst with happiness.

Birthday cake is more delicious with friends to share the birthday wishes!

"M" is for More Birthday Photos . . .

# Very Happy Holidays

Holidays we celebrated and our traditions _____

_____
_____
_____
_____
_____
_____

Place a photo here!

_____
_____
_____
_____
_____

Place a photo here!

Your friendship is the best present ever.

Other holidays we celebrated together _____

_____

_____

_____

_____

_____

_____

_____

_____

_____

_____

_____

_____

_____

_____

_____

Place a photo
here!

© Disney

# Holiday Photos

# Daily Adventures

Who took care of me during the day _____

How I spent my days _____

_____

_____

Baby-sitters _____

Playmates _____

Playgroups _____

_____

Preschool _____

Address _____

Name of teacher _____

My first day _____

_____

My friends _____

_____

Experiences to remember _____

_____

_____

After-school play _____

_____

_____

_____

"P" is for Pooh who                    loves to ask "why?"

# Discovering and Learning

Elementary School _____

Address _____

My first day of school _____

_____

How we felt _____

_____

_____

Kindergarten _____

Teacher _____

Best friends _____

What I enjoyed the most _____

_____

_____

Special accomplishments _____

_____

_____

After school play _____

_____

_____

_____

_____

© Disney

# "M" is for Moments with You...

As a baby I was _____

_____

_____

_____

_____

_____

_____

_____

I laughed when _____

_____

_____

_____

_____

_____

_____

_____

I cried when _____

_____

_____

_____

_____

_____

_____

_____

_____

© Disney

# We'll Never Forget!

My cutest gestures _____
_____
_____

My funniest mispronunciations _____
_____
_____
_____

My creativity _____
_____
_____
_____
_____
_____

Favorite stories about me _____
_____
_____
_____
_____
_____
_____
_____

Sweet dreams, little one.

Pooh tried and tried to stay awake,

but his sleepy eyes had other plans.

© Disney